by
DIK BROWNE

First published 1988 by Attica Publications.

Attica Limited,
DLM House,
Edinburgh Way,
Harlow,
Essex,
CM20 2HL.
England.

ISBN 1 85176 147 0

Printed in U.K.

VI-KING (n.): One skilled in pillaging, sacking and ravaging while retaining charm and grace.

NOW, HOLD IT ONE SECOND

THERE ARE A COUPLE OF THINGS I THINK YOU SHOULD KNOW

DID YOU KNOW THAT YOU LOSE ALL THE GOOD OF VEGETABLES IF YOU WASH THEM ?

OR THAT WATER CAUSES MOST SHIPWRECKS AND FLOODS ?

AND I ALSO HEARD THAT EXPENSIVE CLOTHING CAN BE RUINED BY SOAKING IN HOT WATER
© 1987 King Features Syndicate Inc World rights reserved

AND BELIEVE IT OR NOT ... MOST ACCIDENTS OCCUR IN THE FAMILY BATHROOM

NO DICE ?
SNAKE EYES !
DIK BROWNE
4-26

"...WHEN THE DARK BEGINS TO LOWER, COMES A PAUSE IN THE DAY'S OCCUPATION, KNOWN AS...

"THE HAPPY HOUR"
MERLIN'S BAR

HEY! HAMLET, PRINCE OF DENMARK! HOW YA' DOING ?
DON'T ASK

I CAME HOME FROM COLLEGE TO FIND MY FATHER SLAIN AND MY EVIL UNCLE MARRIED TO MY FOOLISH MOTHER...

MY FATHER'S GHOST NOW WALKS THE BATTLEMENT AT NIGHT AND MY GIRLFRIEND OPHELIA HAS GONE MAD! MAD! MAD!

NOW, THAT'S A **TRAGEDY**!
IT'S THE WORST SPRING BREAK I EVER HAD!
6-7
DIK BROWNE

WELCOME
TO
FRIENDLYTOWN
NO
LOITERING
KEEP
OFF
GRASS
KEEP
OUT
BEWAR
OF DOG

BAR
NO
VIKINGS

BAR
NO VIKINGS

BAR
NO VIKINGS

BAR
VIKINGS
DIK BROWNE
11-30
©1986 King Features Syndicate Inc.

NO DESSERT FOR ME.
THIS SALAD WILL DO
YES, MA'AM

HMMM... I COULD
HAVE A TAD...

I'D LIKE TWO SCOOPS OF
COCONUT-FUDGE RIPPLE

ON A BAVARIAN-FUDGE CAKE
WITH ORANGE-SPICE ICING

SMOTHERED IN CANDY SPRINKLES, HONEY SAUCE AND...

SOME SWISS-MOCHA MORAVIAN-NUT CREME CAFE EXPRESSO ON THE SIDE

DIK BROWNE
© 1987 King Features Syndicate, Inc. World rights reserved

...AND A DOGGIE BAG FOR THE GUILT!
4-19

THIS GOLD COIN DOESN'T SOUND RIGHT!
PFTZ!

WELL, I GUESS THERE'S ONLY ONE WAY TO TELL...

CHOMP!

IS THIS COIN ANY GOOD?

CHOMP!

CHEW
CHEW
CHEW

CHOMP!

DELICIOUS
5-31
DIK BROWNE
© 1987 King Features Syndicate, Inc. World rights reserved

THIS WAS MY LUCKY DAY! I WON A RACE, FOUND A GOLD COIN AND HELGA KISSED ME!
HOW WAS YOUR DAY, LUCKY EDDIE ?

DON'T ASK

THIS WAS THE WORST DAY OF MY LIFE... FIRST I BROKE A SHOELACE...

THEN I WAS CALLED IN FOR BACK TAXES

THEN I HAD A DISAGREEMENT WITH MY GIRL-FRIEND

AND I WAS ATTACKED BY A SWARM OF ENRAGED BUTTERFLIES!

WHAT A DAY!

THANK GOODNESS, IT'S OVER!
DIK BROWNE 5-17
© 1987 King Features Syndicate Inc World rights reserved

TODAY YOU WILL MAKE HISTORY!
WHY ME?!!

BECAUSE- I BELIEVE IN YOU!

YOU'RE GOING TO BE FAMOUS!

WE'RE NOT GOING TO JUST SHOOT AN APPLE OFF YOUR HEAD

WE'RE GOING TO MAKE THEM FORGET ABOUT WILLIAM TELL !

WE'RE GOING FOR THE **LONG-DISTANCE** RECORD! JUST REMEMBER...

DON'T MOVE!
DIK BROWNE
© 1987 King Features Syndicate Inc. World rights reserved
8-23

IT IS A STRANGE, MYSTICAL NIGHT... FULL OF PORTENTS

BUT WHO ARE THOSE GUYS ?

BROTHER OLAF! WHAT ARE YOU DOING OUT SO LATE ?

WE'RE WAITING FOR A SIGN!
REALLY ?!
WOW...

HERE IT COMES!
HEY! IT LOOKS GREAT!
MONASTERY
8·30
DIK BROWNE

REMEMBER— DON'T EMBARRASS ME!
PTUI
WELCOME VIKINGS AND VIKING WIVES!

VIKINGS **AND** THEIR WIVES TOGETHER FOR THE ANNUAL BASH!
ISN'T IT FUN? I DON'T KNOW **WHY** WE DIDN'T DO THIS SOONER!
USE YOUR NAPKIN AND GET THOSE ELBOWS OFF THE TABLE!

BRING US A SALAD—AND PUT ON SOME DECENT CLOTHES!

© 1987 King Features Syndicate, Inc. World rights reserved
NOW! NOW!! NO SINGING AT THE DINNER TABLE!

DON'T SLURP! AND TAKE THAT SPOON OUT!
WE'LL JUST HAVE SOME MINERAL WATER
I KNOW WHY WE DIDN'T DO THIS SOONER!
9-6
DIK BROWNE

OH MY! AN ENCHANTED FOREST!
AND LOOK! A WISHING WELL!
WISHING WELL

WISHING WELL

© 1987 King Features Syndicate, Inc. World rights reserved

ING
L

WISHING WELL
I WANT MY MONEY BACK!
DIK BROWNE 11-1

IT HAPPENS EVERY TIME ...

IT ALWAYS RAINS WHEN I FORGET MY UMBRELLA!

I'M HUNGRY! GIMME LUNCH!!

SPLAT!

HOW ABOUT A TOSSED SALAD ?
8-2

THERE'S A LOT TO BE SAID FOR YOUR HAGAR...HE'S HARDWORKING ...LOYAL ... JOLLY...

AND ONE THING MORE...
HE'S MINE!

WHAT'S HAGAR'S SECRET ?
HAGAR HAS CHARISMA

I JUST HEARD THAT HAGAR HAS CHARISMA!
WOW!

HAGAR HAS CHARISMA!
CHARISMA?!!

GUESS WHAT?! HAGAR HAS CHARISMA!
© 1987 King Features Syndicate, Inc. World rights reserved

HAGAR, I'M YOUR BEST FRIEND, SO I HAVE TO TELL YOU SOMETHING...
DIK BROWNE
10·25

I HAVE **CHARISMA**, DOCTOR! IS THAT SERIOUS?!!

ON A DAY LIKE THIS, IT'S IMPORTANT TO FIND THE RIGHT TREE...

IT SHOULD HAVE GOOD SHADE AND A SONGBIRD OR TWO...
LIKE THIS

IS THIS WHAT MAMA CALLS "LOAFING"?
NOT NECESSARILY

SOME PEOPLE MIGHT SAY SO...BUT ON THE OTHER HAND—

I MIGHT ALSO BE SITTING HERE WORKING HARD... THINKING ABOUT SOME BIG IMPORTANT PROBLEM...

...LIKE THE MEANING OF LIFE, OR WAR AND PEACE... OR HOW TO FIND THE WILD BEES' HONEY... OR STUFF LIKE THAT...

SO ALWAYS REMEMBER THIS, MY SON...

IT AIN'T LOAFING UNLESS THEY CAN PROVE IT
© 1987 King Features Syndicate, Inc. World rights reserved
DIK BROWNE 4-12

NO PLACE TO GO, NOTHING TO DO... BORING!

LET'S TELL JOKES
OKAY! YOU GO FIRST!

DID YOU HEAR THE ONE ABOUT THE KING OF SPAIN, THE GIRAFFE, THE ELEPHANT, THE DWARF, THE MOUSE, THE GRANDFATHER'S CLOCK, THE RABBIT, THE APPLE PIE AND THE PRINCESS ?
NO!

WELL ?

I CAN'T REMEMBER THE PUNCH LINE...
DIK BROWNE
6-14

I WONDER WHY HELGA HAS A DUCK LIKE "KVACK" FOR A PET ?

EVERYBODY'S GOT A PET THESE DAYS—
IT'S A FAD

HERE COMES COYER THE LAWYER
WITH A DOG!

WHAT'S HIS BREED?

HE'S A "LEGAL-BEAGLE"
IS HE SMART ?

WATCH THIS!
FETCH YOUR LEASH!

NO! NO! THAT'S A LEASE!
DIK BROWNE
12-7

WHAT HAPPENED, HAGAR ?
JUST WHAT I EXPECTED !

I TOLD LUCKY EDDIE NOT TO WORRY ABOUT FIGHTING THE GIANT !

I TOLD HIM TO GET UP CLOSE AND AIM THE SLINGSHOT AT THE GIANT'S FOREHEAD!

I TOLD HIM, "THE BIGGER THEY ARE, THE HARDER THEY FALL!!"
WHERE'S LUCKY EDDIE NOW?

THE GIANT FELL ON HIM
1-11
DIK BROWNE

I AM KING OF THE HILL!
NO!

YES!
NO!

YES!

NO!

YES!

NO!

YES!

MAYBE
DIK BROWNE
11-15
© 1987 King Features Syndicate, Inc. World rights reserved

I THINK "GRUDGES" ARE STUPID AND A WASTE OF TIME!
OH, YEAH?

WELL, I LIKE 'EM!

DAD, WHAT DO YOU DO WITH A "GRUDGE"?
THAT DEPENDS...
© 1987 King Features Syndicate, Inc. World rights reserved

YOU CAN CARRY A GRUDGE

OR HOLD A GRUDGE AGAINST SOMEONE

OR HAVE A GRUDGE MATCH

YOU CAN EVEN NURSE A GRUDGE
DIK BROWNE
2-1

HAVE YOU EVER HAD A GRUDGE ?
OH... A FEW

KA-BOSH!
OH, OH!

MY LUNCH!!

I'M MAD AS #@☆!!!
AND I'M NOT GOING TO TAKE IT ANYMORE!!

I'LL SAY THIS FOR HAGAR — HE DOESN'T HOLD EVERYTHING INSIDE
LAZY!
NO GOOD!
SLOPPY!

IN A WAY, I THINK THAT'S HEALTHIER — DON'T YOU?
!!

NOT FOR US...
HA
DE
DA
DIK BROWNE
1-4
© 1987 King Features Syndicate, Inc. World rights reserved

DID YOU SAY SOMETHING?
YOU KNOW, I THINK YOU'RE RIGHT!
GRRRRR...

I'D BETTER CHECK IT OUT

HOW'S THE SOUP COMING?
HMMMM...NEEDS SALT

NEEDS PEPPER

NEEDS GARLIC AND FLOUR

AND A LITTLE PAPRIKA
HOW IS IT NOW ?

SIP

11-16
NEEDS SOUP
DIK BROWNE

SURPRISE! LUTE AND I HAVE DECIDED TO GET MARRIED!

BUT, LISTEN TO THE BEST PART —

OUR WEDDING IS GOING TO BE DIFFERENT... LUTE IS WRITING THE WHOLE CEREMONY!

CAN YOU READ SOME, LOVEY?
OKAY, BUT IT'S STILL A LITTLE ROUGH

"I TAKE THIS MAN TO BE MY **MASTER**... LORD OF MY DESTINY... **KING** OF ALL HE SURVEYS...

"I PLEDGE TO SERVE HIS EVERY **WHIM**, AND TO WORK TIRELESSLY FROM NOW ON TO MEET HIS SUPERIOR NEEDS"

SPLAT!
BAM

I SAID IT WAS A LITTLE ROUGH
1-25
DIK BROWNE

TWACK!

AHHH...
A VALENTINE.

EVERYBODY LOVES ST. VALENTINE'S DAY.

EVERYBODY !

© 1987 King Features Syndicate Inc. World rights reserved

DIK BROWNE
2-15

IT'S A LOVELY WEEKEND— WHAT WOULD YOU LIKE TO DO ?
OH... THE USUAL

SIGH THAT'S WHAT I THOUGHT

EVERY WEEKEND IS THE SAME... HE SITS THERE, DRINKS SUDS AND LOOKS AT THAT DUMB PICTURE!

HE COULD BE PLANTING A ROSE GARDEN... OR IMPROVING HIS MIND...OR TAKING ME DANCING— BUT NO!
BURP!

MEN HAVE NO IMAGINATION!

WOULDN'T IT BE PERFECT IF THAT PICTURE COULD MOVE?
DIK BROWNE
11-8

WHERE'S LUCKY EDDIE TONIGHT ?
HE'S GONE TO DR. ZOOK'S FOR HALLOWEEN

WELL, I GUESS IT'S TIME TO SUMMON THE DEMONS ...
WOW! YOU CAN DO THAT?

YOU CAN CALL UP EVIL SPIRITS AND MONSTERS ?

THAT'S SO COOL! YOU ACTUALLY TOUCH THE ETHEREAL PLANE!
©1986 King Features Syndicate, Inc. World rights reserved

CAN I WATCH?
SURE
DIK BROWNE
10-26

LUNCH!
GEE, I THOUGHT THERE'D BE MORE TO IT

YOU'VE GOT A NICE WIFE WHO KEEPS A NICE HOME– YOU'RE LUCKY!
I KNOW

HELGA REMINDS ME OF IT FROM TIME TO TIME

IT MUST BE FUN TO BE MARRIED!
THAT DEPENDS

DEPENDS ON WHAT ?
DEPENDS ON HOW LONG YOU'VE BEEN MARRIED

THE LONGER YOU'RE MARRIED, THE MORE FUN IT IS !!
DIK BROWNE
7-12

OH, GOODNESS GRACIOUS!!
OH, WOW!

HAGAR! HAGAR!
MORE TROUBLE!

HEY! I MEAN...ER... THE ENEMY...WOW... HEY...ER...
HOLD IT!!

THINK FIRST—THEN TALK!

© 1987 King Features Syndicate, Inc World rights reserved

OH, NEVER MIND! JUST TALK!!
DIK BROWNE
2-22

I SUDDENLY FEEL A STRANGE AND POWERFUL ATTRACTION !!
WHAT COULD IT BE ?!
CAKES

WOW! BAVARIAN FUDGE CAKE !!

HEY, MISTER, HOW MUCH ARE YOUR CAKES ?

CAKES ?! WE DON'T MAKE "CAKES"! WE MAKE FINE PASTRIES— TEMPTING DESSERTS, DELIGHTFUL DIVERSIONS !

50 KOPECKS

THAT'S A LITTLE HIGH

HOW MUCH FOR THIS DEMONSTRATOR MODEL ?
11-9
DIK BROWNE
© 1986 King Features Syndicate Inc World rights reserved

RAIN! RAIN! RAIN!!
WELL, THE FARMERS LOVE IT

I'LL BET THE FARMER'S **WIFE** HATES IT!
COULD BE...

WHAT A STUPID DAY!
YEAH... NOTHING TO DO...

MAYBE WE COULD DO SOMETHING WITH OUR HAIR...
MAYBE COLOUR IT?

THIS HOUSE COULD USE COLOUR!
WE COULD PAINT IT PURPLE

AND MOVE ALL THE FURNITURE AROUND!!
AND PAINT AND DO HAIR!

AND WASH SNERT!
WHERE'S DADDY ?
DIK BROWNE
3-15

WOMEN ARE DANGEROUS ON A RAINY DAY
© 1987 King Features Syndicate, Inc World rights reserved

"AN IMPORTANT ANNOUNCEMENT"

COME ON! IT MIGHT BE A SALE!
AW, IT'S PROBABLY ANOTHER ONE OF THE KING'S CRAZY IDEAS!

HERE IS THE LATEST LIST OF WORDS NOT TO BE UTTERED IN KING NOVGOROD'S REALM
HUH! MORE CENSORSHIP!!

"ALL WORDS THAT START WITH THE LETTER '___.'"
WHAT? WHAT LETTER?

I CAN'T TELL YOU. EVEN TO SAY THE LETTER IS PROHIBITED BY LAW

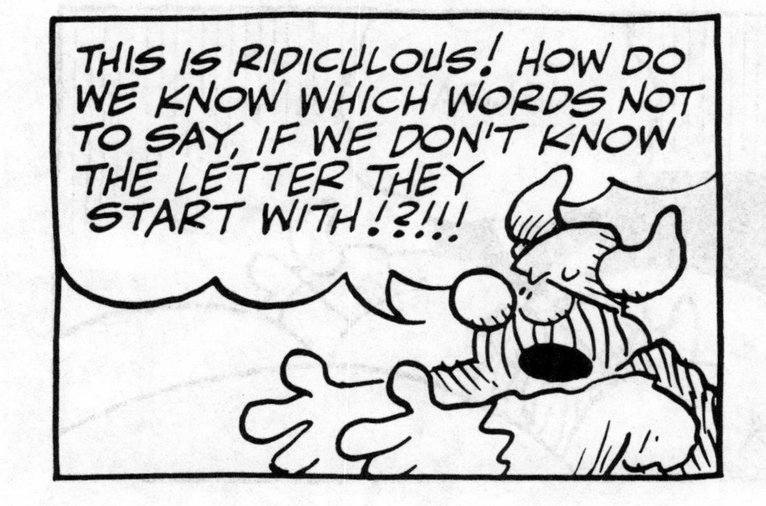
THIS IS RIDICULOUS! HOW DO WE KNOW WHICH WORDS NOT TO SAY, IF WE DON'T KNOW THE LETTER THEY START WITH!?!!!

DIK BROWNE
5-3
YOU'LL JUST HAVE TO UESS
?
?

SIGH

HELGA...

PSSST,
HELGA...

HELGA

PSSST, HELGA

HELGA!

WHAT?!
© 1987 King Features Syndicate, Inc. World rights reserved

I CAN'T SLEEP
DIK BROWNE 1-18

COME ON! IT'S TIME TO GO!
BUT I'M TIRED

YOU'RE ALWAYS TIRED! THIS MEETING WILL STIMULATE YOU

DO WE **HAVE** TO GO TO THIS THING?
YES! BECAUSE THE 'NOTHING BUT THE TRUTH' SOCIETY CAN BE VERY IMPORTANT

IF PEOPLE TOLD THE TRUTH, IT WOULD BE A BETTER WORLD... THERE'D BE LESS HATE... MORE LOVE... LESS STRESS...

ALL WE HAVE TO DO IS TELL EACH OTHER HOW WE **REALLY** FEEL!

HOW ARE YOU GOING TO DO THAT?
I DON'T KNOW...
DIK BROWNE
6-21

TONIGHT'S OUR FIRST MEETING
NOTHING BUT THE TRUTH SOCIE
HOW DARE YOU!
THAT'S A LIE!
YOU ARE FAT!
THAT'S AN INSULT!
© 1987 King Features Syndicate, Inc. World rights reserved

THE PARTY'S OVER! WHEN ARE YOU GOING TO GET OUT OF THAT BED AND FACE THE NEW YEAR ?!

IT AIN'T A QUESTION OF "WHEN," BUT "CAN" I GET UP?!

THE ONLY WAY I CAN FACE GETTING UP IS DOING IT ONE STEP AT A TIME...

DIK BROWNE
© 1988 King Features Syndicate, Inc. World rights reserved
FIRST I SIT UP...

THEN I PUT ONE FOOT ON THE FLOOR...

THEN I PUT THE OTHER FOOT ON THE FLOOR...

NOW I AM ABLE TO TAKE ON ONE MORE DAY, FULL OF MEAN, COLD ENEMIES IN A HOSTILE WORLD

GET BACK ON THE FLOOR, YOU COWARD!
1-3

HELGA AND HONI SURE LOVE TALKING TO EACH OTHER, DON'T THEY ?
BEWARE OF BARGAINS...
BARGAINS

OF COURSE—THAT'S HOW GIRLS LEARN FROM THEIR MOTHERS

HOW DO YOU FIND A GOOD ONE ?
REALLY GOOD ONES ARE HARD TO FIND AND THEY'RE GETTING RARER
SOLD

THE TRICK IS TO GET ONE IN NOT GOOD SHAPE... PERHAPS EVEN A MESS...
CHEAP

BUT WITH A LOT OF WORK AND TENDER, LOVING CARE YOU CAN MAKE OVER A MESS INTO YOUR PRIDE AND JOY

BOY! HELGA SURE KNOWS REAL ESTATE!
NAW... SHE'S TALKING ABOUT MEN!
FOR RENT
DIK BROWNE
6-28

IT'S FUN BEING A VISIGOTH...

YOU DON'T MEAN VISIGOTH—
YOU MEAN VIKING!
WHAT'S THE DIFFERENCE?

ARE YOU KIDDING? YOU DON'T KNOW THE DIFFERENCE BETWEEN A VIKING AND A VISIGOTH?!!
NO...

VIKINGS ARE BRAVE, BOLD HEROES... AFRAID OF NOTHING!

VISIGOTHS ARE SWARMY CREEPS WHO FILCH AND SNITCH!

VIKINGS ARE GREAT! VISIGOTHS ARE NOTHING! NOW DO YOU UNDERSTAND?!
YES...

© 1987 King Features Syndicate Inc. World rights reserved

SO, ARE WE VIKINGS OR VISIGOTHS?
3-29
DIK BROWNE

YOU'RE A GOOD DOG, SNERT, BUT—

WE HAVE TO BRUSH UP ON YOUR OBEDIENCE TRAINING

SIT UP!

SPEAK!

GIVE ME YOUR PAW!

PLAY DEAD!
© 1987 King Features Syndicate, Inc. World rights reserved

DIK BROWNE
I KNEW IF I KEPT TRYING I'D DISCOVER ONE HE COULD DO!
7-5

SHIP AHOY!
WHERE?

HARD APORT ON THE LARBOARD SIDE BEARING LEFTWARD AND A BIT...
NEVER MIND

IS THAT A FRIENDLY OR A HOSTILE SHIP?
GEE... HARD TO SAY...

FIRE A WARNING SHOT ACROSS HER BOW

PING
© 1987 King Features Syndicate Inc World rights reserved
DIK BROWNE 7-19

BAM!
BOP!
ZOK

PROBABLY HOSTILE

I'M HUNGRY! FEED ME! FEED ME!
IN A MINUTE, DEAR

HE GETS VERY FUSSY IF I DON'T FEED HIM ON TIME!

I WANT MY SPECIAL PLATE!
OH! YOUR SPECIAL PLATE! INDEED! YOU'RE SUCH A BABY!

I AM NOT A BABY!
HERE'S YOUR SPECIAL PLATE AND HERE'S YOUR DINNER

I WON'T EAT IT!
WHY NOT?

YOU SAID I WAS A BABY! I **HATE** THAT!
ALL RIGHT! ALL RIGHT! YOU'RE NOT A BABY! THERE!

GOOD

CAN I HAVE MY BOTTLE?
DIK BROWNE
7-26

La NOUVELLE CUISINE
AH! HERE'S THAT NEW PLACE! LET'S TRY IT!
MENU
YE OLDE CUISINE

WHAT'S THE SPECIALTY OF THE HOUSE ?

IT'S CALLED "Blarg"

WHAT AN UNUSUAL NAME! WE'LL HAVE FOUR OF THEM
VERY GOOD, MADAM!
DIK BROWNE

WELL! THIS SHOULD BE A REAL CULINARY ADVENTURE
IF YOU SAY SO!

GEE! I WONDER WHY THEY CALL IT "BLARG"?

BLARG!!
8-9
© 1987 King Features Syndicate, Inc. World rights reserved

JUST RUNNING DOWN TO THE LOCAL STORE FOR SOME MORE HORRIBLY GOOD CARTOON BOOKS, COLOUR ALBUMS, CALENDARS, DIARIES, REMINDER CALENDARS, GREETING CARDS, GIFTWRAP AND TAGS – ALL FEATURING ME OF COURSE!

WHY NOT JOIN ME BEFORE THE BARBARIANS GET THERE!

Hagar Books to Collect:

POCKET BOOKS

Hagar Tries Again
Hagar Has A Go
Hagar In A Fix
Hagar On The Rampage
Hagar Gets It All
Hagar In The Rough
Hagar Leads The Way
Hagar Takes A Break
Hagar All At Sea
Hagar On Holiday

COLOUR ALBUMS

Hagar Lets Himself Go
Hagar In Trouble
Hagar The Hero

COLOUR CARTOON BOOKS

Hagar Tells It Like It Is
Hagar Never Say Die

BLACK + WHITE CARTOON BOOKS

Hagar Meets His Match
Hagar In A Hurry

Available Soon...

Hagar The Horrible's Viking Handbook